# MAKING THE GRADE

EASY POPULAR PIECES FOR YOUNG VIOLINISTS. SELECTED AND ARRANGED BY JERRY LANNING. EDITED BY MARJORY KING

## VIOLIN PART

Exclusive Distributors:
Music Sales Limited
Newmarket Road, Bury St. Edmunds, Suffolk IP33 3YB.
This book © Copyright 1995 Chester Music.
ISBN 0-7119-5055-5
Order No. CH61087
Cover design and typesetting by Pemberton and Whitefoord.
Music engraved by Seton Music Graphics Ltd.
Printed in the United Kingdom by
Caligraving Limited, Thetford, Norfolk.

## Chester Music
(A division of Music Sales Limited)
8/9 Frith Street, London W1V 5TZ

# INTRODUCTION

This collection of 14 popular tunes has been carefully arranged and graded to provide attractive teaching repertoire for young violinists. The familiarity of the material will stimulate pupils' enthusiasm and encourage their practice.

The technical demands of the solo part increase progressively up to the standard of Associated Board Grade 3. The piano accompaniments are simple yet effective and should be within the range of most pianists.

Practical suggestions for fingering are given, but these may of course be adapted to suit the needs of the individual student. It is important always to feel a steady pulse, so that bow speeds can be planned appropriately.

# CONTENTS

# THE INCREDIBLE HULK (THEME FROM)

*Composed by Joe Harnell.*

This theme from the TV series is a wistful and attractive melody, which reflects the gentle side of the Hulk's nature, so bow very lightly through the slurs.

# YESTERDAY

*Words & Music by John Lennon & Paul McCartney.*

Most peoples' favourite Beatles song. Notice the F sharp and G sharp in the ascending
scale of A melodic minor (bar 4), followed by the F and G naturals in the descending scale.
The fingering relates to first and third positions, but if you feel daring try the whole piece in second position.

# SUMMERTIME

*By George Gershwin, Ira Gershwin, DuBose & Dorothy Heyward.*

'Summertime' is probably Gershwin's most famous tune. The notes aren't difficult,
but be careful that you play the correct rhythm in bars 11 and 12.
Play the long notes with vibrato if possible.

# EL CONDOR PASA (IF I COULD)

*Musical Arrangement by J. Milchberg & D. Robles. English Lyric by Paul Simon.*

This is a traditional melody from South America, made popular by Simon and Garfunkel.

Keep a very steady tempo.

# YELLOW SUBMARINE

*Words & Music by John Lennon & Paul McCartney.*

This Beatles number needs to be played with a tight, accurate rhythm — don't slip into triplets in the chorus, and don't use too much bow. Notice that the verse is repeated an octave higher.

# BRIDGE OVER TROUBLED WATER

*Words & Music by Paul Simon.*

Here is Paul Simon's most enduring song.

Try for a full, rounded tone as the piece builds to a climax around bar 23.

# ITSY BITSY, TEENIE WEENIE, YELLOW POLKADOT BIKINI

*Words & Music by Lee Pockriss & Paul J. Vance.*

If you want to leave out the spoken sections, you can cut from the first beat of bar 10 to the second beat of bar 12, and cut bar 22 completely. Watch out for the $\frac{2}{4}$ bar.

# JEANIE WITH THE LIGHT BROWN HAIR

*Words & Music by Stephen Foster.*

This song needs really expressive playing.

Be particularly careful of the slurred ninth (A to B) in bar 14. The B should be really soft.

Don't grip the neck too tightly when you change position.

# I KNOW HIM SO WELL

*Words & Music by Benny Andersson, Tim Rice & Bjorn Ulvaeus.*

Many of the notes are slurred in pairs,
which should be practised carefully to ensure that the bow is shared equally between both quavers.

# ONE MOMENT IN TIME

*Words & Music by Albert Hammond & John Bettis.*

Make sure your bow speed is appropriate for the varying durations of each bow.

# BIRDIE SONG / BIRDIE DANCE

*Words & Music by Werner Thomas & Terry Rendall.*

Articulate the quavers in the first section clearly, playing off the string if you can.

If not, grip the string with little bows for a similar effect.

# HE AIN'T HEAVY HE'S MY BROTHER

*Words by Bob Russell. Music by Bobby Scott.*

Some of the rhythms are a bit tricky in this piece. If you have trouble with them,
practise each phrase slightly slower, counting in quavers. Be careful to count the rests in bar 21.

# AMERICA

*Music by Leonard Bernstein. Lyrics by Stephen Sondheim.*

In this lively number from 'West Side Story' the time signature alternates between $\frac{6}{8}$ and $\frac{3}{4}$;
you will need to keep this clearly in mind in bars 17 to 25.
In the latter section push the up bows before the accented notes.

# THE ENTERTAINER

*By Scott Joplin.*

This piano rag featured in the film 'The Sting'. Make sure you keep a very steady tempo.
You will find that the piece is quite a test of stamina.

11/02 (46032)

# MAKING THE GRADE · GRADE 3

**EASY POPULAR PIECES FOR YOUNG VIOLINISTS. SELECTED AND ARRANGED BY JERRY LANNING. EDITED BY MARJORY KING**

Exclusive Distributors:
Music Sales Limited
Newmarket Road, Bury St. Edmunds, Suffolk IP33 3YB.
This book © Copyright 1995 Chester Music.
ISBN 0-7119-5055-5
Order No. CH61087
Cover design and typesetting by Pemberton and Whitefoord.
Music engraved by Seton Music Graphics Ltd.
Printed in the United Kingdom by
Caligraving Limited, Thetford, Norfolk.

## Chester Music

(A division of Music Sales Limited)
8/9 Frith Street, London W1V 5TZ

# INTRODUCTION

This collection of 14 popular tunes has been carefully arranged and graded to provide attractive teaching repertoire for young violinists. The familiarity of the material will stimulate pupils' enthusiasm and encourage their practice.

The technical demands of the solo part increase progressively up to the standard of Associated Board Grade 3. The piano accompaniments are simple yet effective and should be within the range of most pianists.

Practical suggestions for fingering are given, but these may of course be adapted to suit the needs of the individual student. It is important always to feel a steady pulse, so that bow speeds can be planned appropriately.

# CONTENTS

# THE INCREDIBLE HULK (THEME FROM)

*Composed by Joe Harnell.*

This theme from the TV series is a wistful and attractive melody, which reflects the gentle side of the Hulk's nature, so bow very lightly through the slurs.

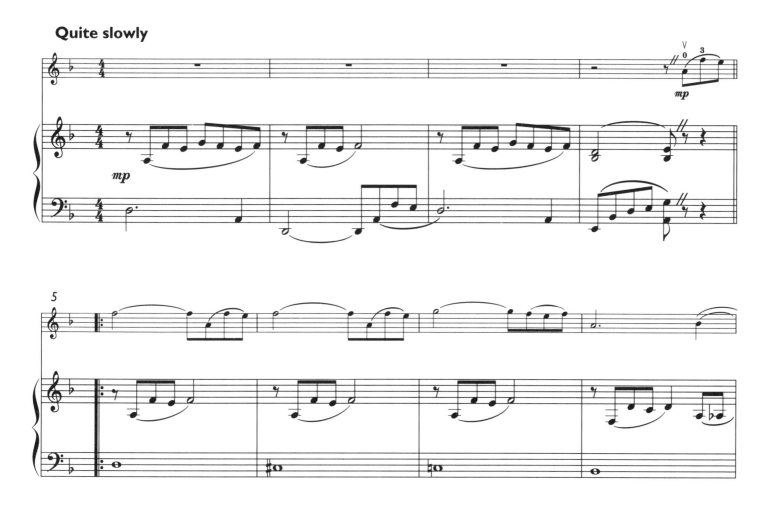

# YESTERDAY

*Words & Music by John Lennon & Paul McCartney.*

Most peoples' favourite Beatles song. Notice the F sharp and G sharp in the ascending
scale of A melodic minor (bar 4), followed by the F and G naturals in the descending scale.
The fingering relates to first and third positions, but if you feel daring try the whole piece in the second position.

**Moderately**

# SUMMERTIME

*By George Gershwin, Ira Gershwin, DuBose & Dorothy Heyward.*

'Summertime' is probably Gershwin's most famous tune. The notes aren't difficult,
but be careful that you play the correct rhythm in bars 11 and 12. Play the long notes with vibrato if possible.

**Moderately slow**

# EL CONDOR PASA (IF I COULD)

*Musical Arrangement by J. Milchberg & D. Robles. English Lyric by Paul Simon.*

This is a traditional melody from South America, made popular by Simon and Garfunkel.

Keep a very steady tempo.

# YELLOW SUBMARINE

*Words & Music by John Lennon & Paul McCartney.*

This Beatles number needs to be played with a tight, accurate rhythm — don't slip into triplets in the chorus, and don't use too much bow. Notice that the verse is repeated an octave higher.

# BRIDGE OVER TROUBLED WATER

*Words & Music by Paul Simon.*

Here is Paul Simon's most enduring song.

Try for a full, rounded tone as the piece builds to a climax around bar 23.

**Not too fast**

# ITSY BITSY, TEENIE WEENIE, YELLOW POLKADOT BIKINI

*Words & Music by Lee Pockriss & Paul J. Vance.*

If you want to leave out the spoken sections, you can cut from the first beat of bar 10 to the second beat of bar 12, and cut bar 22 completely. Watch out for the $\frac{2}{4}$ bar.

Two, three four, Tell the peo-ple what she wore.

Two, three, four,

Stick a - round we'll tell you more.

# JEANIE WITH THE LIGHT BROWN HAIR

*Words & Music by Stephen Foster.*

This song needs really expressive playing.

Be particularly careful of the slurred ninth (A to B) in bar 14. The B should be really soft.

Don't grip the neck too tightly when you change position.

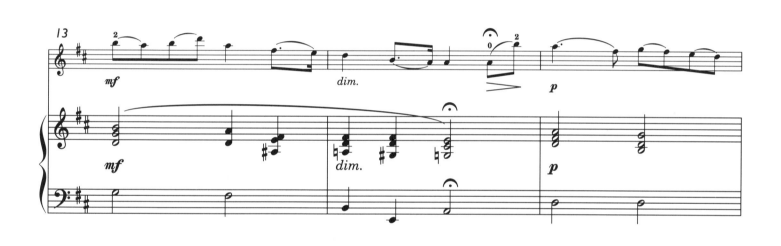

# I KNOW HIM SO WELL

*Words & Music by Benny Andersson, Tim Rice & Bjorn Ulvaeus.*

Many of the notes are slurred in pairs,
which should be practised carefully to ensure that the bow is shared equally between both quavers.

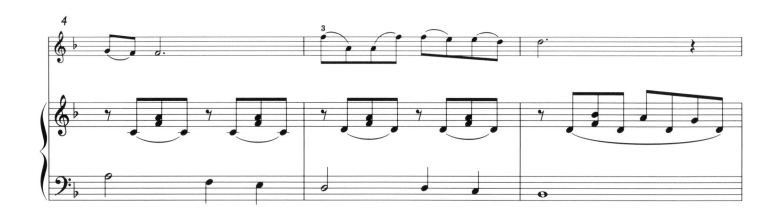

# ONE MOMENT IN TIME

*Words & Music by Albert Hammond & John Bettis.*

Make sure your bow speed is appropriate for the varying durations of each bow.

# BIRDIE SONG / BIRDIE DANCE

*Words & Music by Werner Thomas & Terry Rendall.*

Articulate the quavers in the first section clearly, playing off the string if you can.

If not, grip the string with little bows for a similar effect.

# HE AIN'T HEAVY HE'S MY BROTHER

*Words by Bob Russell. Music by Bobby Scott.*

Some of the rhythms are a bit tricky in this piece. If you have trouble with them,
practise each phrase slightly slower, counting in quavers. Be careful to count the rests in bar 21.

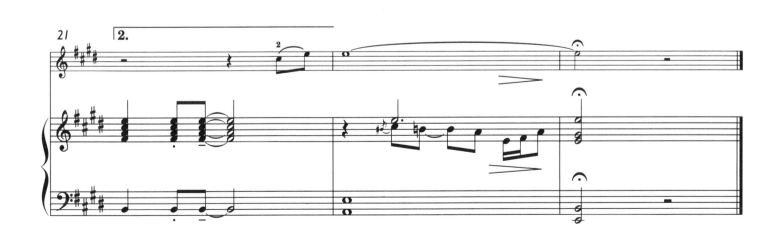

# AMERICA

*Music by Leonard Bernstein. Lyrics by Stephen Sondheim*

In this lively number from 'West Side Story' the time signature alternates between $\frac{6}{8}$ and $\frac{3}{4}$;
you will need to keep this clearly in mind in bars 17 to 25.
In the latter section push the up bows before the accented notes.

# THE ENTERTAINER

*By Scott Joplin.*

This piano rag featured in the film 'The Sting'. Make sure you keep a very steady tempo.
You will find that the piece is quite a test of stamina.

11/02 (46032)